3

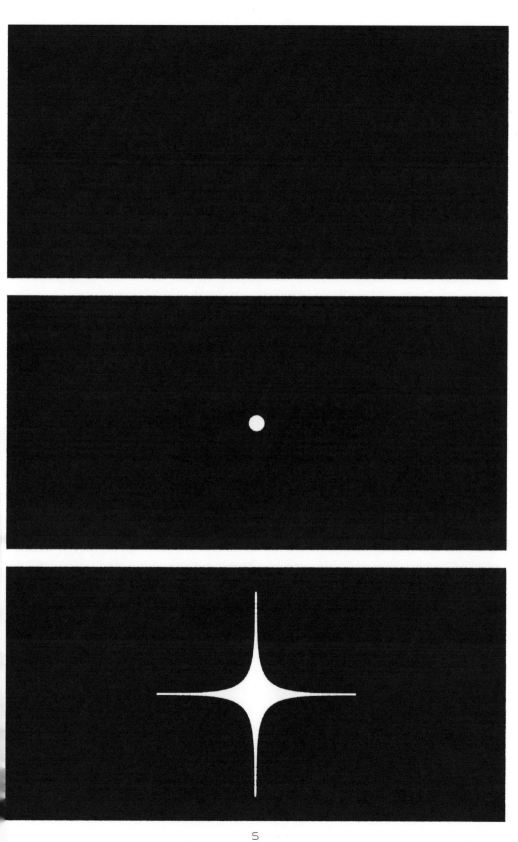

5

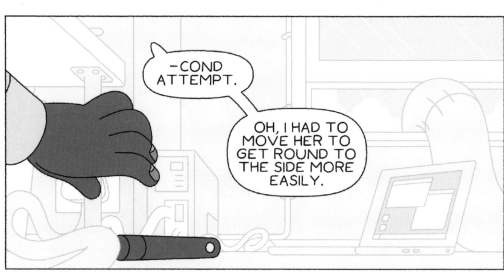

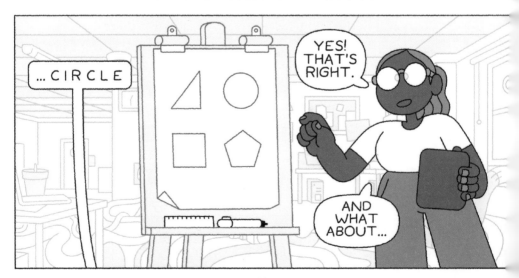

27

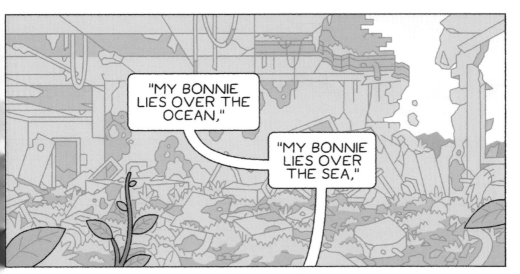

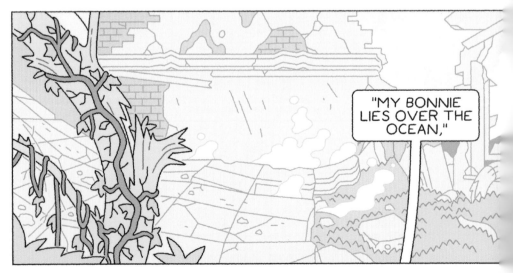

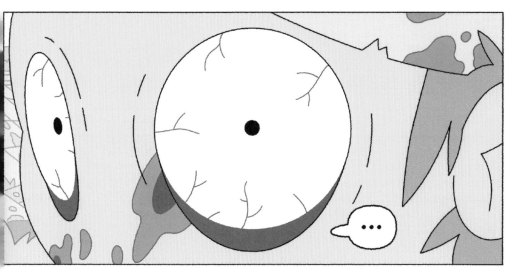

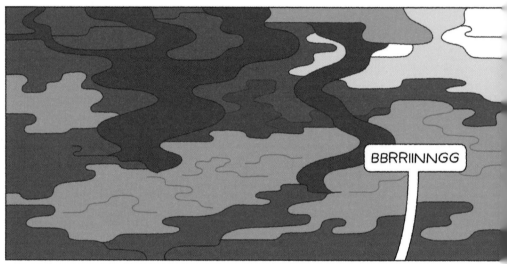

CONCEPT ART

"SALLY" →

SALLY'S CREATOR ←

THESE ARE SOME SKETCHES I MADE OF VERONICA AND DAISY (THEN "SALLY") WHILE COMING UP WITH THE BASIC CONCEPT FOR THE STORY.

VERONICA CAME OUT HOW I WANTED PRETTY MUCH FIRST TIME - OR MAYBE I WAS JUST TOO LAZY TO CHANGE HER.

STORY THUMBNAILS

THESE ARE THE FIRST SET OF ROUGH DRAWINGS I DID IN SEQUENCE TO PLAN OUT THE STORY BEATS - YOU CAN SEE THE IDEA OF THE WHOLE THING BEING TOLD FROM DAISY'S FIXED POINT OF VIEW WAS IN THERE FROM PRETTY EARLY ON. THIS VERSION OF THE STORY IS QUITE DIFFERENT AFTER THE APOCALYPSE, THOUGH - I PLANNED FOR DAISY TO BE FOUND AND POTENTIALLY WORSHIPPED BY A POST-APOCALYPTIC TRIBE, AND THEN LATER ABDUCTED BY ALIENS. THIS WAS ALL CUT FOR TIME AND SIMPLICITY.

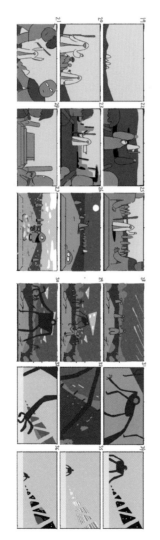

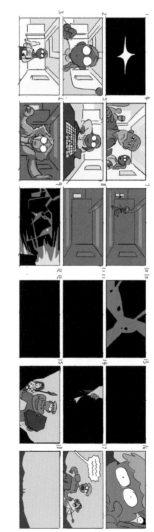

ROUGH PAGES

I ROUGHED OUT THE WHOLE COMIC LIKE THIS IN
ADOBE ANIMATE (FORMERLY FLASH), A PROGRAM
I OFTEN USE IN ANIMATION. THE DRAWINGS HERE
ARE BARELY STICK FIGURES, BUT YOU CAN STILL
USUALLY TELL IF THE STORY WORKS AT THIS
STAGE.

THE DIALOGUE IS COLOUR-CODED TO MAKE UP
FOR THE LACK OF CLARITY IN THE DRAWING. I
TWEAKED THE SCRIPT REPEATEDLY AFTER THIS
POINT.

COLOUR THUMBS

ONCE I DECIDED THAT THE LAST SEGMENT OF THE COMIC WOULD INVOLVE A LONG
TIMELAPSE, I REALISED THIS WOULD CALL FOR A TON OF COLOUR CHANGES TO INDICATE
THE PASSAGE OF TIME. DIFFERENT TIMES OF DAY, DIFFERENT WEATHER CONDITIONS,
THAT KIND OF THING. THE SCRIPT BELOW LOOKS PRETTY BUT IT WAS ACTUALLY A
HUGE FAFF TO GET WORKING IN THE FINISHED STORY – THE PANELS NEEDED TO BE
DISTINCT TO GET THE FEEL OF A FLICKERING TIMELAPSE BUT THEY ALSO STILL KIND OF
NEEDED TO LEAD INTO ONE ANOTHER, THEY COULDN'T JUST BE RANDOM.

JOE SPARROW IS AN ANNIE-
AWARD-WINNING AND EISNER-
NOMINATED WRITER, ARTIST
AND ARGUABLE HUMAN WHO
MAKES ANIMATION AND COMICS.

HE LIVES AND WORKS IN
LONDON, ENGLAND.

SHORT BOX 2023